£6.99

TOM and JERRY™

ANNUAL 2005

This book belongs to:

Name: ....

Age: ....

Address: ....

....

....

....

CAT AND MOUSE! CONTENTS:

Cat or Mouse?!

Our dynamnic duo's shadows are all mixed up! Can you match up the pictures with the correct shadows?

Answers on page 61

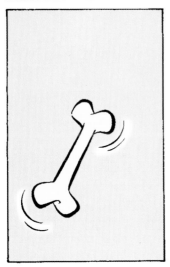

THOSE BONE THROWERS MUST BE HERE SOMEWHERE!

YUMMY! SLURP!

YUMMY! FAT, PLUMP MICE!

YUMMY! YUMMY!

SMACK! MUNCH!

LUNCH TIME!

OH!

CRACK!

YOU'VE GORGED YOURSELVES! NOW IT'S MY TURN! ROAR!

HURRY UP, TUFFY! LET'S HIDE IN THIS CAVE!

OH, IT'S VERY DARK IN HERE!

PUST PUST

THIS CAVE WON'T SAVE YOU! CAN'T YOU SEE THAT IT'S BIG ENOUGH FOR ME TOO!

TOO BAD THE KIDS THOUGHT I WAS THEIR DADDY! IT WOULD HAVE BEEN MUCH WORSE IF THE MOTHER HAD MISTAKEN ME FOR HER HUSBAND!

I'M LUCKY! I GUESS THEY LOST ME!

AARRRGH!

EH?

GOBBLE!

TICKLE, TICKLE, TICKLE!

HA HA HA!

SPLAT!

13

CONTINUED ON PAGE 23

In the Dog House!

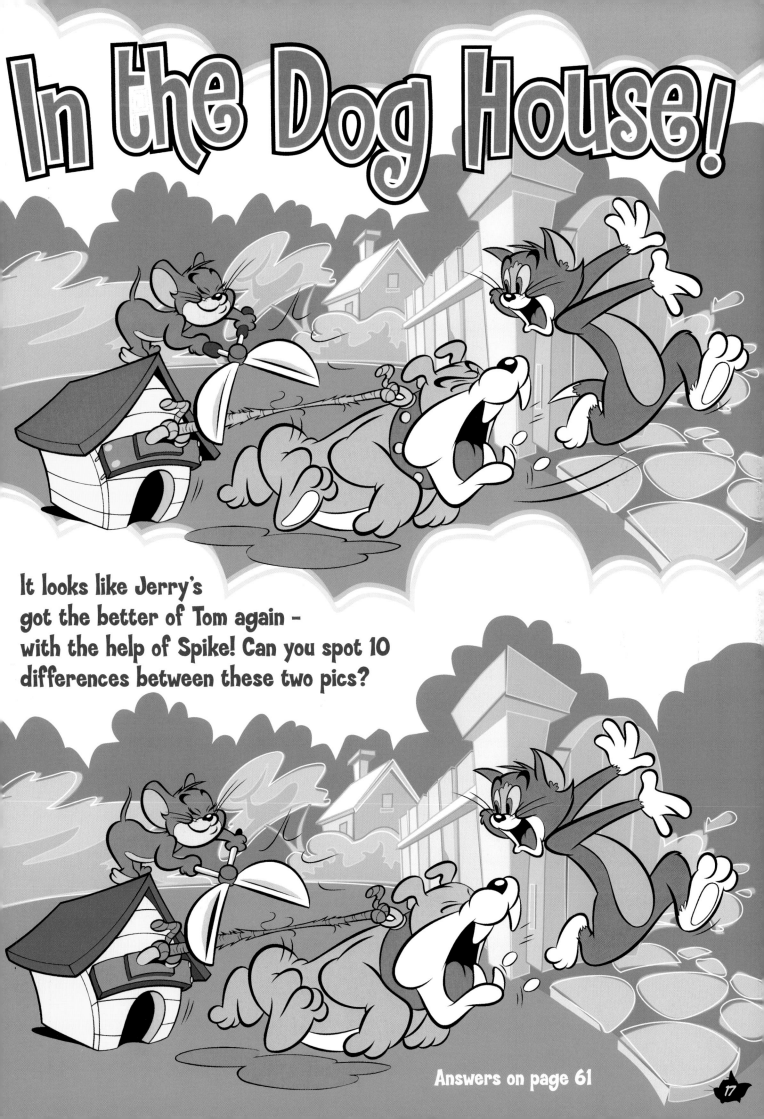

It looks like Jerry's got the better of Tom again - with the help of Spike! Can you spot 10 differences between these two pics?

Answers on page 61

17

THE END

FOOTY FUN!

Being aspiring footy stars themselves, Tom and Jerry have put together heaps of sporty puzzles for you!

ON THE BALL!

Jerry's on the ball - are you? Can you find all 12 words hidden in this grid?

C	O	R	N	E	R	P	H	G	S
P	M	Y	E	V	I	D	T	D	L
O	I	K	S	D	V	R	E	N	I
Q	W	I	C	R	T	L	L	E	D
Y	D	C	H	I	P	Y	K	B	E
E	U	K	G	B	R	J	C	L	P
L	M	D	J	B	U	T	A	I	P
L	M	H	G	L	F	W	T	K	L
O	Y	U	Y	E	T	F	I	A	P
V	Y	M	Q	R	E	D	A	E	H

KICK
VOLLEY
BEND
DUMMY
SLIDE
DIVE
CORNER
TACKLE
HEADER
DRIBBLE
CHIP
HAT TRICK

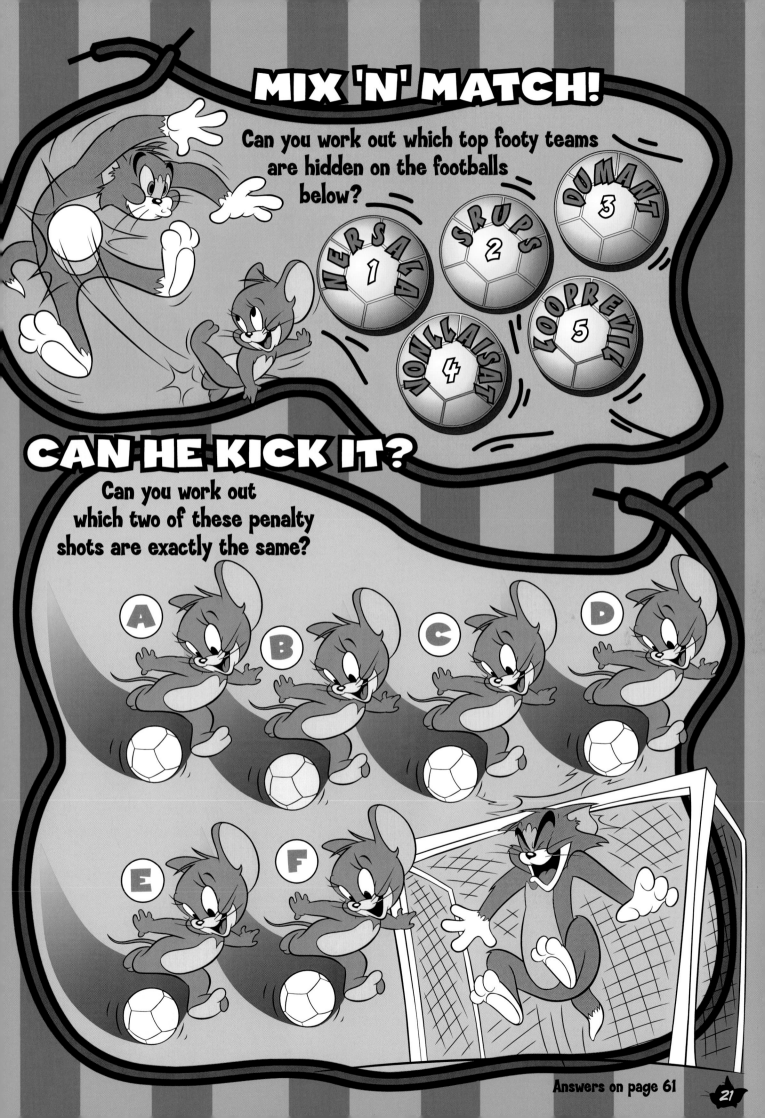

MIX 'N' MATCH!

Can you work out which top footy teams are hidden on the footballs below?

1. NERSAAL
2. SRUPS
3. DUMANT
4. VONLLAISAT
5. KOOPREVIIL

CAN HE KICK IT?

Can you work out which two of these penalty shots are exactly the same?

A   B   C   D

E   F

Answers on page 61

21

Somethin' Fishy!

Tom makes a big *mouse*-take when he tries to get his hooks into Jerry! Can you fill in the blanks in the rhyme below?

Tom was going fishing,
He had his hook and ☐☐☐☐,
"But not for fish," he chuckled,
"That mouse will soon be mine!"

As Jerry sat beside the lake,
Tom hid high up a tree,
Then dangled cheese for tasty bait,
To catch the ☐☐☐☐☐ for tea!

But Jerry took the fishing line,
"I'll see ☐☐☐ gets a bite!"
He grinned and tied it to a rock,
Tom tugged with all his might.

The rock went flying through the air,
And struck him on his ☐☐☐.
"That caught you out!" grinned Jerry,
While Tom was mighty sore!

22

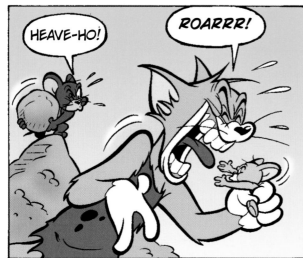

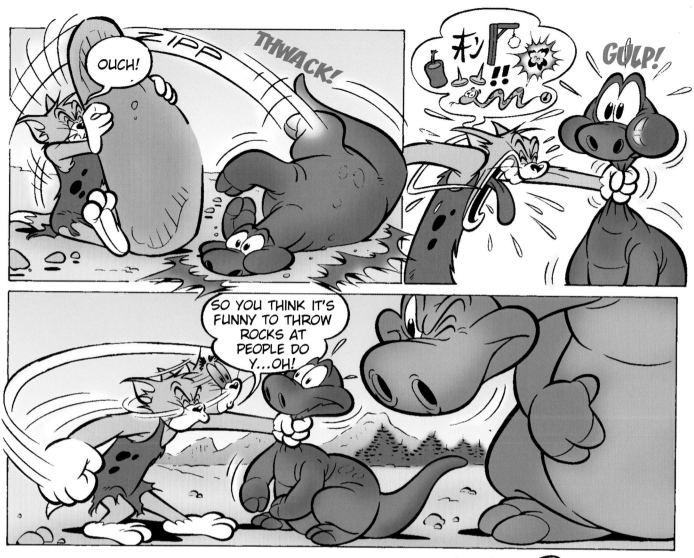

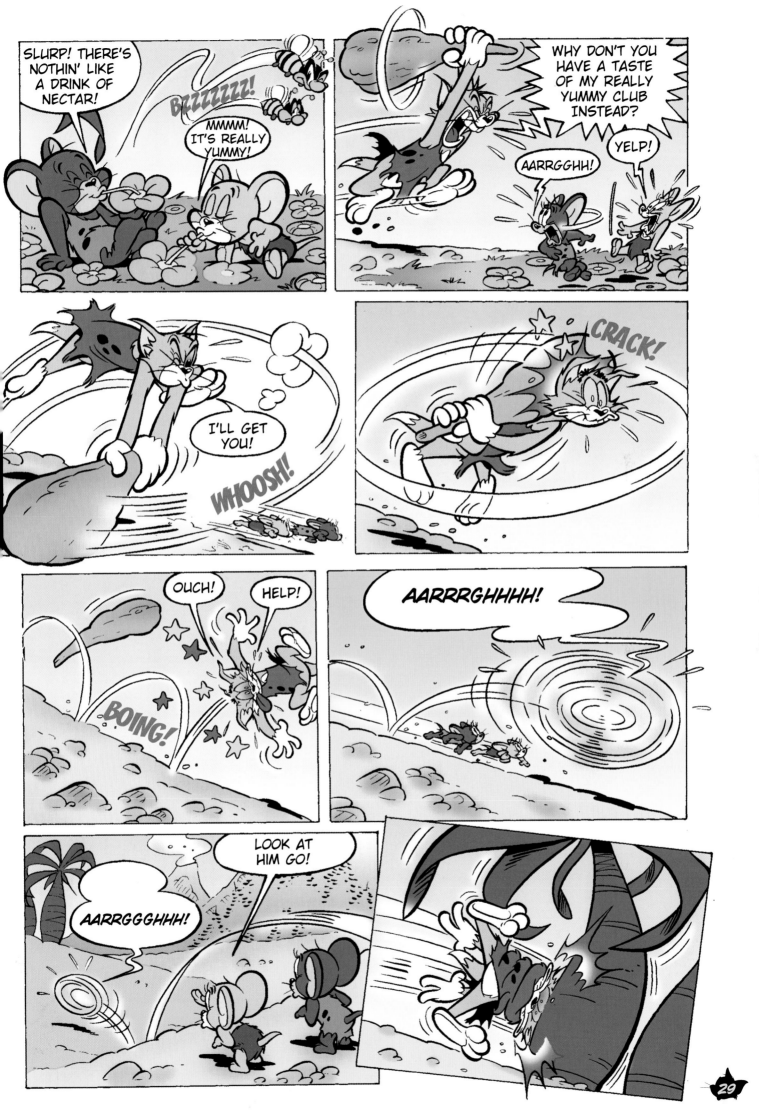

OUCH! I DON'T HAVE ANY STRENGTH LEFT NOW! I FEEL ALL DIZZY...

EVERYTHING'S GOING ROUND AND ROUND...WAIT!... ROLLING AND ROLLING...

YES! THAT SHOULD DO THE TRICK!

I THINK THIS INVENTION IS GOING TO CHANGE MY LIFE!

CRACK! CRACK!

TA-DAA!

I'LL CATCH THEM! NOTHING CAN STOP ME NOW!

I'M GLAD THAT CAT HAS GONE!

HERE I COME! YOUR TIME IS UP, MICE!

EEEEEK!

!!!

WHAT'S YOUR TOON PERSONALITY?

Which of your three fave Tom and Jerry characters do you shape up to? Try this quick-firing quiz to find out!

1
You see a kid lose a balloon that floats towards you. Do you...
a) Try to catch it and give it back?
b) Burst it for fun 'cos the big BANG's best?
c) Ignore it? Chasing's too much effort!

2
You meet your friends in the burger bar. To tickle your taste buds, do you...
a) Order a burger with mouth-watering double cheese?
b) Always go for your fish favourite?
c) Choose the biggest, mega-meaty burger-bite?

3
The kid-next-door doesn't know he's dropping wrapped sweets from a hole in the bag. Do you ...
a) Help to pick up the sweets and accept just one as a reward?
b) Hope he doesn't spot you scooping them all up for yourself?
c) Make sure no one else helps themselves until the kid fetches another bag to put them in?

4 You visit a stately garden and get stuck in the middle of a giant maze. Would you…

a) Listen for footsteps or voices then try to find your way towards other people who aren't lost?
b) Stand and scream 'HEEEELP!'?
c) Chill out till someone turns up to rescue you?

5 It's raining and there's only room for one more on the bus home. You have an anorak but your friend doesn't. Do you…

a) Flip a coin to see who rides and who walks, wearing the anorak?
b) Jump onto the bus and keep the anorak for when you get off?
c) Say you're happy to walk in the rain?

MOSTLY A'S:
There's no mouse-taking you're like that cheese-lovin' funster Jerry - helpful and fair-minded but quick-thinking and ready for a challenge!

MOSTLY B'S:
Don't blame your friends if sometimes they s-cat-ter when you show. Just like Tom, sometimes you forget to put your friends first!

MOSTLY C'S:
Like Spike, you're laid back, generous and care about the little guys. Nothing seems to worry you. But everyone sits up if you bark because they know you can bite!

CODE BREAKER!

Always one for a bit of detective work, Jerry's created a coded message for Tom! See if you can work out what he says by looking at the key and filling in the boxes.

Check out page 53 to learn how to make your own secret messages!

Answers on page 61

34

WHAT WOULD I DO WITHOUT MICE? THIS IS GREAT!

YEAH, YOU CAN HAVE SO MUCH FUN WITH THEM!

I THINK WE'VE PLAYED ENOUGH FOR TODAY! HOW ABOUT A LITTLE APPETISER BEFORE DINNER?

GREAT IDEA, MAN. GREAT IDEA!

STOP!

WHAT?!

W-WHO ARE YOU?!

I'M BAT-MOUSE!

OUFF!

WHAM!

OUCH!

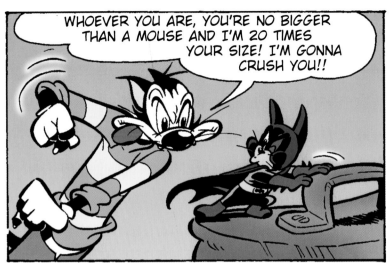

WHOEVER YOU ARE, YOU'RE NO BIGGER THAN A MOUSE AND I'M 20 TIMES YOUR SIZE! I'M GONNA CRUSH YOU!!

YOU'RE GONNA CRUSH ME?

YOU SEEM TO BE SMART, BAT-MOUSE, BUT LET'S SEE HOW YOU COPE WITH THIS IRON BAR!

GULP!

LISTEN UP, YOU DUMB CAT! AS FROM NOW YOU LEAVE ALL THE MICE *ALONE!* IS THAT *UNDERSTOOD?!*

IF YOU DON'T STOP YOU'LL HEAR FROM ME AGAIN! AND REMEMBER - I'M VERY DANGEROUS WHEN I GET ANGRY!

WHAM!

DO YOU HEAR ME?

OUCH!

WHAT ARE WE GONNA DO NOW? I'D RATHER NOT MEET THAT BAT-MOUSE AGAIN!

MAYBE *WE* CAN'T DO ANYTHING, BUT I BET I KNOW SOMEONE WHO CAN!

HERE WE ARE! NOW, FOLLOW ME!

MEANWHILE, THE BAT-MOUSE IS ON THE LOOK-OUT.

IT'S SUSPICIOUSLY CALM AND QUIET TONIGHT...

WHAT?!

I HEARD THAT THE TOMKER HAS PLANS TO GET RID OF THE BAT-MOUSE!

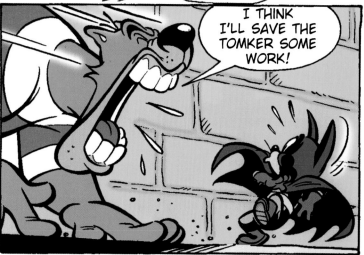

I THINK I'LL SAVE THE TOMKER SOME WORK!

WHY DON'T YOU DISCUSS THE PLANS DIRECTLY WITH ME?

WAH!

YEE-OUCH!

WHAM!

I FHINK I'LL FTICK TO FOOP HEREAFTER!

EH?

YOU'LL REGRET THAT!

MORE WORK FOR THE DENTIST! NOW, BITE HARD!

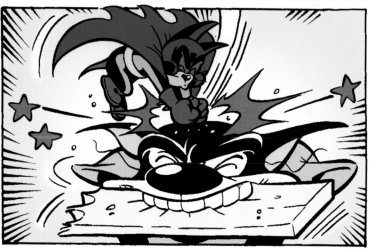

AND NOW...

ZIPP

IT'S TIME FOR YOU TO TELL ME *EVERYTHING!*

OK, BUT DON'T HIT ME ANY MORE! WE ONLY KNOW THAT THE TOMKER IS PUTTING SLEEPING-DROPS FOR MICE IN ALL THE MILK AT THE DAIRY WHERE THEY MAKE THE CHEESE. AND WHEN THE MICE EAT THE CHEESE, THEY WILL SLEEP FOR YEARS!

I SEE!

IF THE TOMKER FINDS OUT THAT WE SNITCHED ON HIM TO THE BAT-MOUSE, WE'RE GONNA BE SORRY!

SHALL WE EMIGRATE TO AUSTRALIA?

42

CONTINUED ON PAGE 54

CLUELESS CROSSWORD

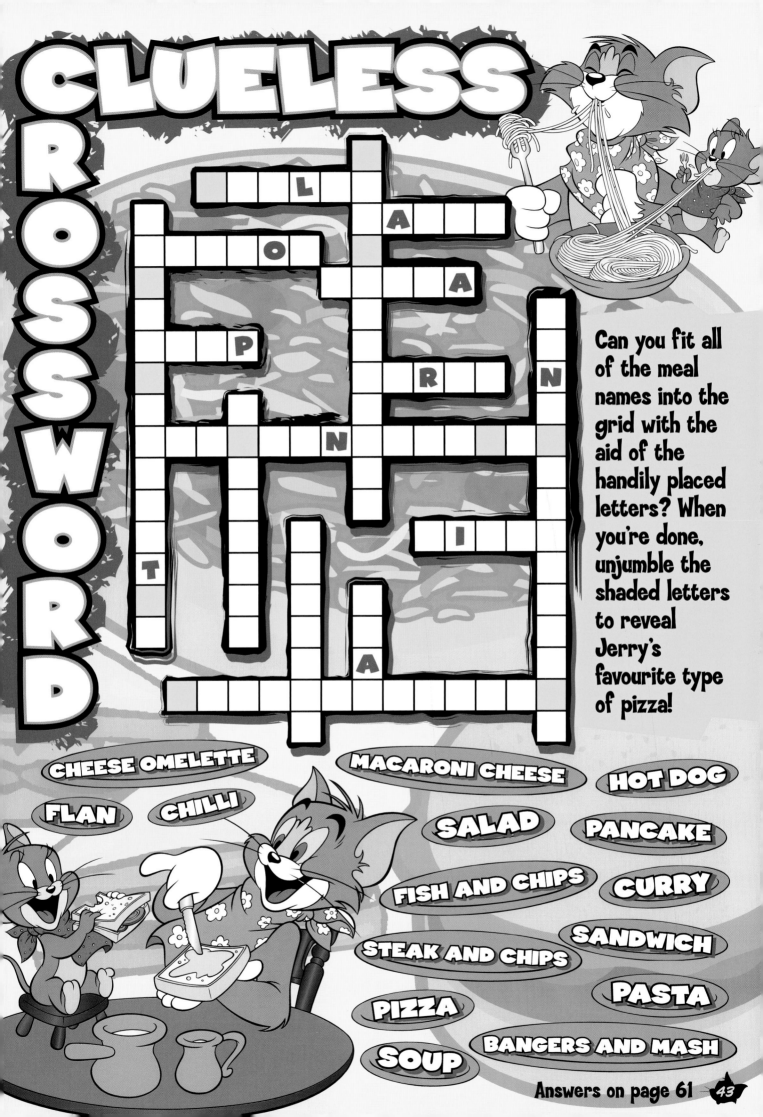

Can you fit all of the meal names into the grid with the aid of the handily placed letters? When you're done, unjumble the shaded letters to reveal Jerry's favourite type of pizza!

CHEESE OMELETTE

MACARONI CHEESE

HOT DOG

FLAN

CHILLI

SALAD

PANCAKE

FISH AND CHIPS

CURRY

STEAK AND CHIPS

SANDWICH

PIZZA

PASTA

SOUP

BANGERS AND MASH

Answers on page 61

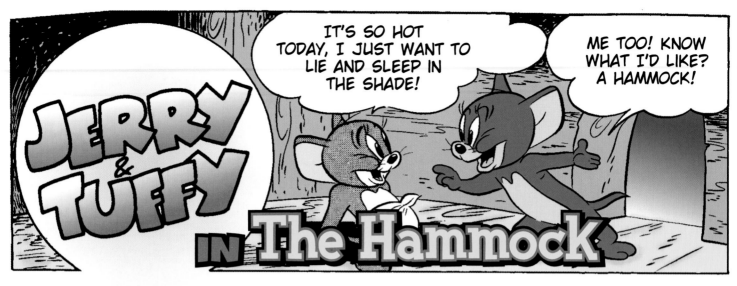

JERRY & TUFFY in The Hammock

IT'S SO HOT TODAY, I JUST WANT TO LIE AND SLEEP IN THE SHADE!

ME TOO! KNOW WHAT I'D LIKE? A HAMMOCK!

JERRY! WE'LL MAKE ONE OUT OF THIS TABLECLOTH!

GREAT! THROW IT DOWN TO ME, TUFFY!

TIE THE TASSELS LIKE THIS!

OKAY!

I'LL TIE MY END TO THIS TREE, AND YOU TIE YOURS TO THE OTHER!

CAN'T DO IT! IT'S NOT LONG ENOUGH!

GRUNT! *GROAN!*

MAYBE WE CAN STRETCH IT TO THIS POLE OVER HERE!

NOPE! CAN'T DO THAT EITHER!

LET'S SEE...

THE END

45

CHEESY CHALLENGE!

We all know how much Jerry loves cheese! Can you work out which types are his favourite by following the lines to spell them out?

1 ☐☐☐☐☐☐☐☐

2 ☐☐☐☐☐

3 ☐☐☐☐☐☐☐☐

4 ☐☐☐☐☐☐☐☐☐☐☐

5 ☐☐☐☐☐☐☐

Answers on page 61

THE END

IT'S A SECRET!

Jerry always knows how to get the better of Tom, but just to make sure his plans are always a surprise, he likes to make sure they can't be seen! Here's how you do it!

YOU WILL NEED:
A lemon, a bowl, an empty ink fountain pen and a piece of paper.

1. Squeeze the juice from the lemon into a bowl.

2. Take your empty ink fountain pen and dip the nib into the lemon juice.

3. Take a clean piece of paper and write down your secret message. It will appear as if you have not written anything.

4. When you want to see your message again, carefully hold the paper close to something hot, such as a radiator, and your message will be revealed!

WHY NOT TELL A PAL ABOUT THIS TRICK, AND YOU CAN WRITE EACH OTHER SECRET MESSAGES!

CONTINUED FROM PAGE 42

THAT NIGHT ON THE OUTSKIRTS OF TOWN...

HERE'S THE DAIRY, BOYS! LET'S GO!

I SENT THE JANITOR A COUPLE OF FREE TICKETS TO TONIGHT'S ROCK-CONCERT! I WOULD HAVE GONE MYSELF, BUT WORK'S WORK AND SOMEONE'S GOTTA DO IT!

FEEL AT HOME BOYS!

WE'VE GOT ENOUGH SLEEPING-DROPS FOR ALL THE MICE IN THE WORLD! WE MUSTN'T FAIL!

HOLD IT!

I FORBID YOU TO DO THAT!

DRAT! HOW DID YOU FIND OUT ABOUT THIS!

ACTUALLY, IT DOESN'T MATTER - IT'S ALREADY TOO LATE!

IT'S *NEVER* TOO LATE WHEN BAT-MOUSE IS AROUND!

NICE SHOW BAT-MOUSE, BUT THAT TUBE WAS *EMPTY!* HA HA HA!

OH!

BUT *THIS* ONE IS FULL!

LET'S GO, BOYS! WE'RE NOT PAID TO WORK OVERTIME! THE FIRST PART OF OUR GENIUS PLAN IS DONE!

POFF!

IS IT THE PLAGUE? WHEN WILL IT STOP?

WE WILL KEEP YOU INFORMED!

AH!!

If you want your friends to wake up again you must leave the Big City forever! I will meet you at 11 o'clock. I want to say goodbye to you when you are conquered and humiliated!
The Tomker

I HAVE NO CHOICE!

BUT WHAT WILL HAPPEN IF *YOU* LEAVE? WHAT ABOUT WHEN THE MICE WAKE UP? WHO WILL PROTECT THEM FROM THE HORRIBLE CATS?

THE FINAL MOMENT IS GETTING CLOSER...

HE'LL BE HERE SOON!

THERE HE IS! I KNEW HE WOULDN'T LET HIS FRIENDS DOWN!

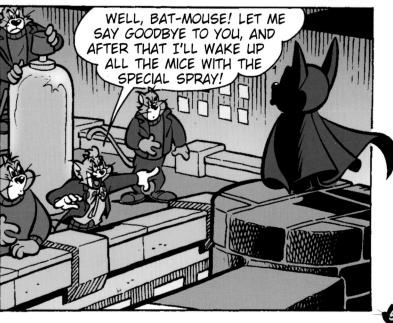

WELL, BAT-MOUSE! LET ME SAY GOODBYE TO YOU, AND AFTER THAT I'LL WAKE UP ALL THE MICE WITH THE SPECIAL SPRAY!

HA HA HA! HE'S LEAVING! I WON!

SHALL I START SPRAYING?

HMM...

NO! I'VE THOUGHT OF SOMETHING MUCH BETTER!

IF I WAS ABLE TO CREATE A SLEEPING DRUG FOR MICE THEN SURELY I CAN MAKE ONE FOR THE REST OF THE CITIZENS OF THE BIG CITY! AND THEN - *THE TOWN WILL BE MINE! HA HA HA!*

BUT... BUT...

I TOLD YOU *NOT* TO SPRAY.

I DON'T BELIEVE IT!

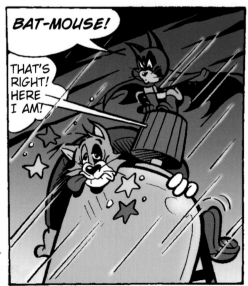

BAT-MOUSE!

THAT'S RIGHT! HERE I AM!

MEANWHILE, THE AWAKENING SPRAY SPREADS ALL OVER THE BIG CITY AND ALL THE MICE WAKE UP!

OUFF!

WHAT HAPPENED?

WHAT A HEADACHE!

LOOK, IT'S BAT-MOUSE! HE MUST HAVE SAVED US!

THE DANGER IS OVER! THE CATS WILL NOT BOTHER YOU FOR A LONG TIME!

THEY HAVE FALLEN INTO A DEEP SLEEP AND WON'T WAKE UP UNTIL WE MICE ARE READY FOR SOME MORE ACTION!

HA HA HA!

THE END!

ANSWERS!

HERE'S YOUR CHANCE TO CHECK OUT HOW YOU DID WITH OUR BRAIN BUSTERS!

PAGE 6

CAT OR MOUSE?!

1E, 2H, 3G, 4F, 5A, 6D, 7B, 8C

PAGE 16

OUT OF TOON!

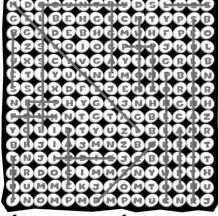

The one Tom made up is Cowbell Hop.

PAGE 17

IN THE DOG HOUSE!

PAGE 20-21

FOOTY FUN!

ON THE BALL!

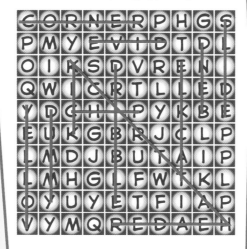

MIX'N'MATCH!

1. Arsenal, 2. Spurs, 3. Man Utd, 4. Aston Villa, 5. Liverpool

CAN HE KICK IT?

D & E

PAGE 22

SOMETHIN' FISHY!

Line, Mouse, Tom, Paw.

PAGE 34

CODE BREAKER!

Bet you can't catch me sucker!

PAGE 43

CLUELESS CROSSWORD

Jerry's favourite type of pizza is a Cheese Feast!

PAGE 46

CHEESY CHALLENGE!

1) Cheddar
2) Gouda
3) Stilton
4) Mozzarella
5) Emmental

PAGE 50

MAZE MANIA!